Bank Account

MATH

REM 5242

AUTHOR: Sue LaRoy

A TEACHING RESOURCE FROM

REMEDIA
PUBLICATIONS

©2019, 2018
Copyright by Remedia Publications, Inc.
All Rights Reserved. Printed in the U.S.A.

www.rempub.com

REMEDIA PUBLICATIONS, INC.
SCOTTSDALE, AZ

This product utilizes innovative strategies and proven methods to improve student learning. The product is based upon reliable research and effective practices that have been replicated in classrooms across the United States. Information regarding the Common Core State Standards this product meets is available at www.rempub.com/standards.

INTRODUCTION

Bank Account Math provides students with an opportunity to improve real-life math skills as they learn about using a bank account.

The first section of this book presents detailed information about bank accounts: what they are, how to apply for one, how to write a check, fill out a deposit ticket use a debit card, fill out a transaction register, read an account statement, do online banking, and responsibly use a bank account. Follow-up activities will test student understanding of important information.

The math section of this book features many practical everyday-life situations involving the use of a checking or savings account and a transaction register. Students will read word problems and decide whether to add, subtract, multiply, and/or divide to arrive at a solution. This book progresses in difficulty. Some activities require students to know how to figure percentages and use fractions. Students will learn how to sign up for online banking, create a PayPal account, and set up an automatic payment using an eCheck.

The vocabulary section consists of a glossary of terms relating to bank accounts. Activities following the glossary serve to test student understanding of the words and phrases. The vocabulary follow-up activities, as well as the review on page 21, may be used as a pre- or post-test.

TABLE OF CONTENT

WHAT IS A BANK ACCOUNT?

A bank account is an agreement made with a bank. You give the bank your money. The bank agrees to take care of it. You can take the money out whenever you want. It is a convenient and safe place to keep your money. You can make **deposits** and **withdrawals**. Most bank accounts include a checking account and a savings account.

Checking Account

A checking account allows for easy **access** to your money. It is the best account to use for everyday spending, paying bills, and depositing money. When you open a checking account, you are given an account number. No two people have the same account number. This number allows the bank to keep track of the activity on your checking account.

Savings Account

A savings account is used to hold your money for future use. Regular deposits into your savings account allow you to save money for a special purchase or a special need. Monthly withdrawals are limited so it's not a good account for everyday use. A savings account has a separate account number from your checking account.

OPENING A BANK ACCOUNT

Before applying for a bank account, you need to gather some items in preparation.

Identification: Most banks require two forms of identification such as a driver's license, passport, Social Security card, state ID, or a birth certificate. This is legal proof that you are who you say you are.

Proof of Address: You will need a lease, mortgage papers, or a utility bill that shows your name and current address.

Opening Deposit: To open a checking and savings account you will need a minimum deposit for each account. Most banks require between $25.00 and $100.00.

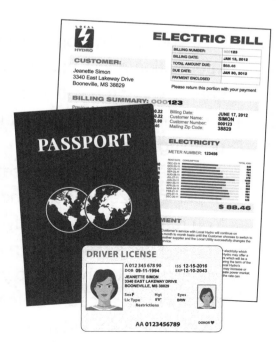

APPLYING FOR A BANK ACCOUNT

You can visit your local bank branch to fill out an application form and present your identification and proof of address. After filling out the form, the bank will review your information. A special credit check will be done that shows your banking history. The bank will then decide whether to approve your application. Most banks will also allow you to fill out an application online.

APPLICANT INFORMATION		
	APPLICANT NAME	
LAST	FIRST	MIDDLE
EMAIL		
ARE YOU AN EXISTING CUSTOMER? ○ YES ○ NO		
ADDRESS & PHONE		
	RESIDENTIAL ADDRESS	
STREET	CITY	STATE
HOW LONG HAVE YOU LIVED AT THIS ADDRESS?	HOME PHONE	BUSINESS PHO

If your application is approved, you will receive papers with important information about your new account. You will be asked to sign a signature card. Every time you write a check or deposit a check your signature will be compared to the signature on this card. Next you will give the bank your opening deposit.

Once your account is set up and your deposit is made, you will get a set of personalized checks and deposit slips. You will also get a **debit card**. You may get these directly from the bank or they may be mailed to you. You will get a **transaction register** to keep track of all the deposits and withdrawals connected to your checking account. Every month the bank will send you an account statement that shows the activity on your checking account. It is important to compare the bank statement with your own records to make sure there are no mistakes.

BANK ACCOUNT APPLICATION

APPLICANT INFORMATION

APPLICANT NAME

Baxter
LAST

Jason
FIRST

Alex
MIDDLE

Baxter45@gmail.com
EMAIL

ARE YOU AN EXISTING CUSTOMER? ○ YES ◉ NO

ADDRESS & PHONE

RESIDENTIAL ADDRESS

1644 NE Cherry St.
STREET

Boise
CITY

ID
STATE

83704
ZIP

3 years, 4 months
HOW LONG HAVE YOU LIVED AT THIS ADDRESS?

208-666-3244
HOME PHONE

208-555-6422
BUSINESS PHONE

208-333-9780
CELL PHONE

MAILING ADDRESS (IF DIFFERENT FROM RESIDENTIAL)

STREET

CITY

STATE

ZIP

PROOF OF ADDRESS ○ RENTAL LEASE ◉ UTILITY BILL ○ MORTGAGE ○ OTHER

CITIZENSHIP & TAX REPORTING STATUS

CITIZENSHIP STATUS ◉ U.S. CITIZEN ○ NON-RESIDENT ALIEN ○ RESIDENT ALIEN

COUNTRY OF CITIZENSHIP(IF NON-U.S. RESIDENT)

COUNTRY OF TAX REPORTING

3/25/92
DATE OF BIRTH

628-33-1244
SOCIAL SECURITY NUMBER

SECURITY INFORMATION

Boise Elementary
NAME OF FIRST SCHOOL ATTENDED

Larsen
MOTHER'S MAIDEN NAME

IDENTIFICATION (RECORD THE DRIVER'S LICENSE OR PASSPORT NUMBER)

Idaho CB654321M

◉ DRIVER'S LICENSE ○ PASSPORT ○ BIRTH CERTIFICATE

Name _____

Use information from pages 1 and 2 to answer the questions.

1.   What is the difference between a checking account and a savings account?

_____

_____

2.   Name two types of identification that the bank needs to open a bank account.

_____

_____

3.   Why do you think it's a good idea to keep your money in a bank account?

_____

_____

4.   How do you prove to the bank what your address is?

_____

_____

5.   Why do you need a transaction register?

_____

_____

6.   How does the bank use a signature card?

_____

_____

7.   How much money do you need to open a checking account?

_____

_____

8.   Name two items you get when your bank account is set up.

_____

_____

USING YOUR CHECKING ACCOUNT

DEPOSITS

Before you can withdraw money, you must **deposit** money into your checking account. Most deposits are made by filling out a deposit slip for the bank. You can also deposit money at an **ATM** or have money automatically deposited into your account electronically.

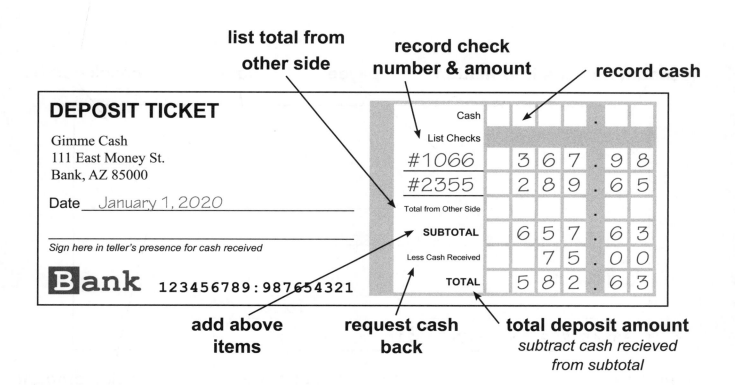

Deposit Slips

A personal deposit slip is printed with your name, address, account number and bank routing number. It has a place to show how much in cash and/or checks you are depositing. There is room to list more checks on the back of the slip. Add the cash and/or checks to get a subtotal. If you are just depositing checks and want some cash back, write in how much cash you want and deduct it from the subtotal. The last line is the total you are depositing.

USING YOUR CHECKING ACCOUNT

CHECKS

Writing a personal check is one way to **withdraw** money from your checking account. You can make purchases and pay bills by writing checks. Printed on your check is your name, address, phone number, check number, **account number**, and the bank's **routing number**.

You will fill in the date, the **payee**, the amount of the check in numbers and in words, write what the check is for, and then sign the check.

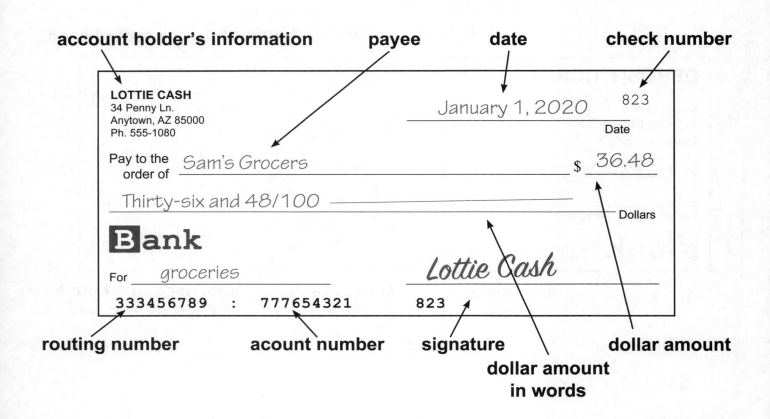

account holder's information   **payee**   **date**   **check number**

LOTTIE CASH
34 Penny Ln.
Anytown, AZ 85000
Ph. 555-1080

January 1, 2020   823
Date

Pay to the order of   Sam's Grocers $ 36.48

Thirty-six and 48/100   Dollars

Bank

For   groceries   *Lottie Cash*

333456789   :   777654321   823

routing number   **acount number**   **signature**   **dollar amount**

dollar amount in words

Research: Ask 5 adults the following questions and write the number of yes answers and the number of no answers.

1. Do you have a checkbook?   _____ Yes   _____ No

2. Do you think it's easy to overspend
    using checks?   _____ Yes   _____ No

3. Do you pay bills with checks?   _____ Yes   _____ No

Name _____

DEPOSIT SLIP PRACTICE

Fill in the blank deposit slip below using the following information. Use today's date. Add to get the subtotal and total. If there is no cash back, these two numbers will be the same.

Cash: $38.90   **Check:** #6502 $188.45   **Check:** #3206 $55.24   **Cash Back:** None

DEPOSIT TICKET		Cash				.		
		List Checks				.		
						.		
Date _____						.		
		Total from Other Side				.		
_____		**SUBTOTAL**				.		
Sign here in teller's presence for cash received		Less Cash Received				.		
Bank 123456789:987654321		**TOTAL**				.		

CHECK PRACTICE

Fill in the blank check using the following information. Sign your name.

Date: Today's Date   **Payee:** Petco   **Amount:** $42.68   **For:** cat food

	4559
_____	Date
Pay to the order of _____	$ _____
_____	Dollars
Bank	
For _____	_____
111456789 : 669654321 4559	

USING YOUR CHECKING ACCOUNT

DEBIT CARD

Another way to withdraw money from your checking account is a debit card. It's a quick and easy way to **access** your account. It has a number that is connected to your checking account. As a security precaution, a 4-digit **PIN** (Personal Identification Number) is assigned to the card. To keep your account safe, do not share your PIN with anyone! Money is immediately withdrawn from your account when using your debit card. It can be used to get cash, make purchases, and pay bills.

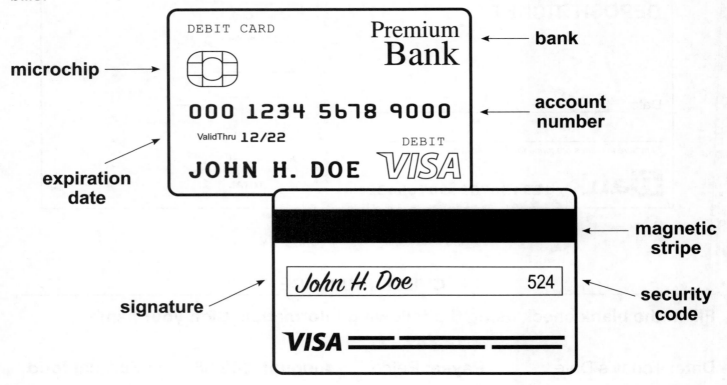

DEBIT CARD VS CREDIT CARD

A debit card looks very similar to a credit card. But is used in a different way. Most debit cards have a small **microchip** on the front. This provides extra security and helps to prevent **fraud**. The front has your name, your debit card number, and an expiration date. It also says "DEBIT." The back has a **magnetic stripe** and a place for your signature. Next to the signature is a 3-digit **security code** that is also used to prevent fraud.

Since your debit card is connected to your checking account, it allows direct access to money that belongs to you. A credit card allows access to money that you are borrowing.

Name _____

Use information from pages 5, 6, and 8 to answer the questions.

1. Name three ways to deposit money into your checking account.

    _____

    _____

2. What is recorded on a deposit slip?

    _____

    _____

3. How is a debit card different from a credit card?

    _____

    _____

4. When using a debit card, how soon is the money taken out of your checking account?

    _____

    _____

5. What are the two ways to write the amount of a check?

    _____

    _____

6. Why do you need a PIN when using a debit card?

    _____

    _____

7. List three things on the front of a debit card.

    _____

    _____

8. Which do you think people use the most often: checks or debit cards? Why?

    _____

    _____

HOW TO USE A DEBIT CARD

You can use your debit card in several different ways. It is important to remember that whenever you use your debit card, money is immediately taken out of your checking account. You should record each transaction!

IN PERSON

When you purchase something in a store you can use your card in a **POS terminal** at the register. You can also use it for transactions at an **ATM**.

MOBILE APP

You can register your debit card to use in mobile shopping apps. Services like PayPal and Venmo also allow you to easily tranfer money to friends and family with your phone.

ONLINE

You can also purchase items online. When it comes time to pay for your purchase, fill out the debit card information at checkout.

Research: Ask 5 adults the following questions and write the number of yes answers and the number of no answers.

1. Do you use a debit card? _____ Yes _____ No

2. Do you think it's easy to overspend using a debit card? _____ Yes _____ No

3. Do you use your debit card to shop online? _____ Yes _____ No

4. Do you think teenagers should have a debit card? _____ Yes _____ No

HOW TO USE AN ATM

An Automated Teller Machine or ATM is an electronic way to access your checking account. Each ATM is a little different, but all ATMs let you get cash, make a deposit, or check your account balance. There are ATMs at banks, grocery stores, drug stores, and many other convenient locations.

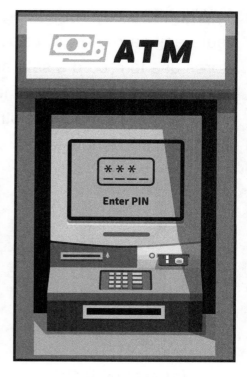

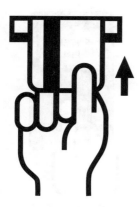

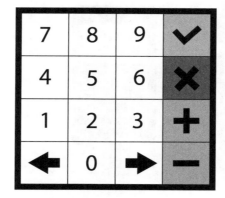

1. Insert Debit Card
Gently slide your debit card into the slot found on the front of the ATM.

2. Enter PIN
Type your 4-digit PIN on the ATM's keypad.

3. Main Menu
Select: withdraw, deposit, or check balance from the main menu. Then follow the prompts.

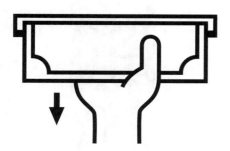

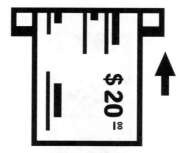

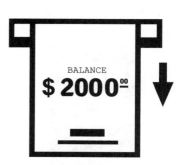

WITHDRAW
To get cash, choose withdraw. Most ATMs only let you get amounts in multiples of $20. Twenty-dollar bills will come out of a slot on the front of the ATM..

DEPOSIT
You can deposit cash or checks into your account. Follow the steps on the screen. Insert the cash or check into a slot on the front of the ATM.

CHECK BALANCE
Check your balance to see how much is in your account. You can view the balance onscreen or have a receipt printed.

HOW TO USE A POS TERMINAL

When you buy something at a store, you can use the POS terminal to pay with your debit card. A POS or point of sale terminal is an electronic card reader that stores use to record a sale and get payment approval. It reads information from the card. Then checks to see if funds are available to pay for the purchase. You will either swipe the magnetic stripe in the terminal or insert the microchip. The following directions show how to use a microchip.

1. Insert Debit Card
Slide the end of the card with the microchip into the slot on the front of the POS terminal. Leave your card in the machine during the transaction.

2. Choose Debit
You will be prompted to choose "Debit" or "Credit." Since you are using a debit card, choose "Debit."

3. Enter PIN
Type your 4-digit PIN on the terminal's keypad.

4. Cash Back
You will be given the option to get cash back. You can choose to get even amounts of cash: $20, $40, $60 or more

5. Approve
You will be asked to verify that the amount being charged is correct. If the total looks right, choose "approve."

6. Remove Debit Card
When the transaction is complete, the machine will make a noise. The screen will prompt you to remove your card.

Name _____

Use information from pages 10, 11, and 12 to answer the questions.

1. List the ways you can use your debit card.

    _____

    _____

2. What three things can you do at an ATM?

    _____

    _____

3. What do you do right after you insert your debit card into the ATM?

    _____

    _____

4. Where can you find ATMs?

    _____

    _____

5. What is a POS terminal?

    _____

    _____

6. What does a POS terminal do?

    _____

    _____

7. What is the next step after inserting your card into the terminal?

    _____

    _____

8. How do you know when the POS transaction is over?

    _____

    _____

TRANSACTION REGISTER

Never write a check or use your debit card unless you have enough money in your checking account to cover the amount you're spending. A **transaction register** is a booklet where you record the withdrawals and deposits for your checking account. By keeping it up to date, you always know your **balance**.

The register has places to record either a check number or a transaction code, the date, a description, the payment or deposit amount, and the balance after each transaction.

Below is a sample transaction register.

AD Automatic Deposit   **AP** Automatic Payment   **ATM** Teller Machine   **DC** Debit Card   **D** Deposit   **T** Transfer

Check# or Code	Date	Description of Transaction	(−) Payment		(+) Deposit		BALANCE 985.00	
1091	4/8	Clark Public Utilities	124	39			860	61
ATM	4/11	Cash Withdrawal	60	00			800	61
AP	4/15	LA Fitness	45	00			755	61
1092	4/15	Meg's Hair Salon	64	87			690	74
AD	4/20	Paycheck			1,875	00	2,565	74
DC	4/21	Lexi's Market	79	28			2,486	46
DC	4/22	Joe's Pizza	24	18			2,462	28
DC	4/26	Walgreen's	18	45			2,443	83
D	4/30	Cash Deposit			65	00	2,508	83

Explain why it's important to keep a transaction register.

_____

_____

_____

RECORDING YOUR TRANSACTIONS

The amount of money available to use in your checking account is called the **balance**. The balance changes after each deposit or withdrawal. After each deposit, you must record it in the transaction register and add the amount to get your new balance. After writing a check or using your debit card, you must record it in the transaction register and subtract the amount to get your new balance.

FILLING OUT A REGISTER

1. Check Number: the number of the check you used

    Transaction Code: use the abbreviation key to record the type of transaction

    AD an electronic deposit made automatically each month

    AP an electronic payment set up to automatically be withdrawn each month

    ATM transactions using an Automated Teller Machine

    DC transactions using a debit card

    D deposits using a deposit slip

    T money electronically transferred from your checking account

2. Date: the day each transaction occurred

3. Description: information about the transaction

4. Payment: the amount subtracted from the balance

5. Deposit: the amount added to the balance

6. Beginning Balance: the amount of money you start out with

7. New Balance: the amount of money you have to spend after each transaction

① Check# or Code	② Date	③ Description of Transaction	④ (−) Payment	⑤ (+) Deposit	BALANCE ⑥ 860.61
ATM	4/11	Cash Withdrawal	60 00		800 61
AP	4/15	LA Fitness	45 00		755 61
1092	4/15	Meg's Hair Salon	64 87		690 74
AD	4/20	Paycheck		1,875 00	2,565 74

BANK ACCOUNT STATEMENT

The bank sends out an account statement each month. It has a listing of all the withdrawals and deposits they have recorded for your checking account. It also shows your available balance at the time the statement was created. By comparing your records with the bank's records each month you will quickly find any mistakes on your account.

TRI-CITIES BANK
CHECKING ACCOUNT STATEMENT

Sebastian Worth
1624 Huntsville Rd.
Florence, AL 35630

Account Number: 5573829007

Beginning Balance: $985.00

Date	Description of Transaction	Withdrawal	Deposit	Balance
4/8	Clark Public Utilities check #1091	124.39		860.61
4/11	ATM Cash withdrawal	60.00		800.61
4/15	LA Fitness AP	45.00		755.61
4/15	Meg's Hair Salon check #1092	64.87		690.74
4/20	Florence School District #65 AD		1,875.00	2,565.74
4/21	Lexi's Market DC	79.28		2,486.46
4/22	Joe's Pizza DC	24.18		2,462.28
4/24	ATM Cash withdrawal	40.00		2,422.28
4/26	Walgreen's DC	18.45		2,403.83
4/30	Cash Deposit		65.00	2,468.83

Above is a sample account statement for the transaction register shown on page 14. Compare the account statement with the transaction register. List any differences.

_____

_____

Name _____

Use information from pages 14, 15, and 16 to answer the questions.

1. What is a transaction register?

   _____

   _____

2. What does the new balance show in a transaction register?

   _____

   _____

   _____

3. Write the meaning of the following codes: AD, AP, DC, and D.

   _____

   _____

   _____

4. In the sample transaction register, what was check #1091 used for?

   _____

5. What was the balance on 4/22 in the sample transaction register?

   _____

6. What does the beginning balance show in a transaction register?

   _____

   _____

7. What is the purpose of an account statement?

   _____

   _____

8. Why is it important to compare an account statement with the transaction register?

   _____

   _____

   _____

ONLINE BANKING

To bank electronically, go to the bank's website to register for online banking. You will need to create a secret **Username** and a **Password**. Then only you can get into your online account. To keep your account safe, do not share this information with anyone! For extra security, you will also be asked 3 or 4 **security questions**.

Each time you want to log in to your account, you will be asked to type in the Username and Password you created. Sometimes you will need to answer one of the security questions before you can see your account.

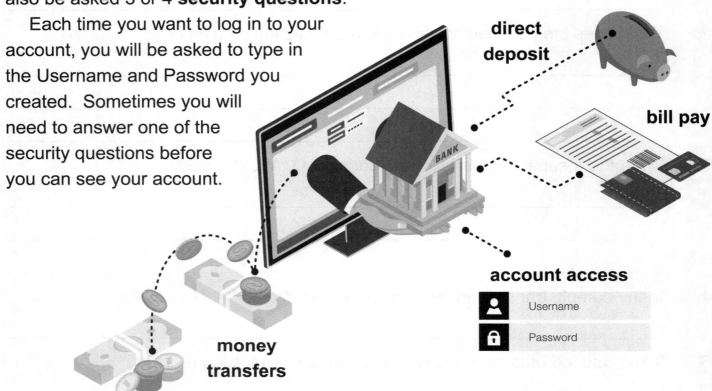

ADVANTAGES OF ONLINE BANKING

Account Access   You have daily access to your account. You can see your current balance and check on withdrawals and deposits. It is the quickest way to find a mistake and fix it.

Money Transfers   You can easily make money transfers from one account to another.

Direct Deposits   You can set up direct deposits that automatically come in to your account on the same day each month.

Bill Pay   You can set up automatic bill pay that allows you to choose a day each month when money is automatically withdrawn from your account to pay a particular bill.

SHOPPING ONLINE

eCHECKS

eChecks are a way to use your checking account electronically. If you purchase something or pay a bill online, you can create an eCheck. Money will be taken directly out of your account. You need your checking account number and the bank's routing number to create an eCheck.

Method of Payment

How would you like to pay?

○ Credit Card   ● eCheck   ○ PayPal

eCheck

Bank Name
U.S. Bank

Bank Routing Number
987654321

Name of Account Holder
Yoshiro Ami

Account Number
123456789

PAYPAL

PayPal is a service that lets you electronically pay, send money, and accept payments in a quick and safe way. Special technology is used to keep your account information secure. You get a PayPal account by creating a Username and Password. Then you register a credit card, debit card or use an eCheck to pay for purchases. When shopping online, most sites include PayPal as an option for payment.

Method of Payment

How would you like to pay?

○ Credit Card   ○ eCheck   ● PayPal

MasterCard   **VISA**   **PayPal** ™

Name _____

Use information from pages 18 and 19 to answer the following questions.

1.   If you want to do your banking electronically, what should you do?

   _____

   _____

2.   Name two things you need to create to set up online banking.

   _____

   _____

3.   What do you need to create an eCheck?

   _____

   _____

4.   How do you log in to your online account?

   _____

   _____

5.   Why is online banking the quickest way to find a mistake on your account?

   _____

   _____

6.   How does automatic bill pay work?

   _____

   _____

7.   What is PayPal?

   _____

   _____

8.   How do you set up a PayPal account?

   _____

   _____

Shade in the letter next to the correct answer.

1. What is a transaction register?
    Ⓐ a place to register your debit card
    Ⓑ a place to record withdrawals and deposits
    Ⓒ a place to register banking mistakes
    Ⓓ none of the above

2. A debit card allows
    Ⓐ direct access to your money
    Ⓑ access to money you are borrowing
    Ⓒ other people access to your money
    Ⓓ the bank access to your money

3. What is a savings account?
    Ⓐ a place the bank holds your money for future use
    Ⓑ a place the bank keeps your money for everyday use
    Ⓒ a place for money that you are borrowing
    Ⓓ none of the above

4. A debit card takes the money out of your account
    Ⓐ in two days
    Ⓑ in two weeks
    Ⓒ in one week
    Ⓓ immediately

5. How much money do you need to open a checking account?
    Ⓐ $500.00 - $850.00
    Ⓑ $400.00 - $500.00
    Ⓒ $25.00 - $100.00
    Ⓓ $1,000.00 - $1,500.00

6. Which of the following lets you safely make payments, send money, and accept payments electronically?
    Ⓐ eBay
    Ⓑ PayPal
    Ⓒ Amazon
    Ⓓ Etsy

7. What is the quickest way to find a mistake in your bank account?
    Ⓐ using online banking
    Ⓑ your transaction register
    Ⓒ using your debit card
    Ⓓ writing a check

8. Which of the following cannot be used as identification to open a bank account?
    Ⓐ a passport
    Ⓑ a driver's license
    Ⓒ a piece of mail with your name
    Ⓓ a birth certificate

Name _____

Solve the problems and fill in the blanks.

1. Ryan bought groceries at Met Market on his way home from work. He bought eggs for $3.29, bread for $4.89, some fruit for $5.87, a salad mix for $3.65 and a roast chicken for $8.99. Add Ryan's purchases.

Fill in the check with today's date, the store name, and the purchase total. Sign the check.

```
┌─────────────────────────────────────────────────────────────────────┐
│  Ryan Watson                                              2011        │
│  335 E. 46th St.                                                      │
│  Kansas City, KS  66102            _____       │
│                                                        Date           │
│                                                                       │
│  Pay to the                                                  $        │
│    order of  _____  _____ │
│                                                                       │
│  _____ Dollars     │
│                                                                       │
│  Bank                                                                 │
│                                                                       │
│  For _____          _____   │
│   123456789  :  987654321       2011                                 │
└─────────────────────────────────────────────────────────────────────┘
```

2. Michelle charges $55.00 per hour for piano lessons. Joe paid her for a one-hour lesson in cash. Cindy wrote her a check (#689) for a two-hour lesson. Rachel also wrote her a check (#1335) for a two-hour lesson. She is depositing the two checks and the cash into her checking account.

Fill in the deposit slip to show her total deposit. Use today's date.

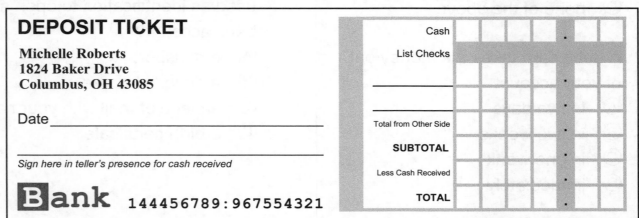

Name _____

Fill in the transaction register below. Add or subtract each transaction to keep a running total of the balance.

Automatic Payment	July 1	Rent	– $1,050.00
ATM	July 3	Cash Withdrawal	– $120.00
Check #105	July 5	Ward County PUD	– $155.00
Check #106	July 8	Met Market	– $27.69
Debit Card	July 10	City Garden Café	– $44.13
Automatic Deposit	July 15	Paycheck	+ $3,450.00
Debit Card	July 18	Rexall Drug Store	– $13.45
Debit Card	July 20	Costco	– $159.85
Debit Card	July 22	Arco Gas	– $32.15
Deposit	July 22	Refund Check	+ $156.98

AD Automatic Deposit   **AP** Automatic Payment   **ATM** Teller Machine   **DC** Debit Card   **D** Deposit   **T** Transfer

Check# or Code	Date	Description of Transaction	(–) Payment		(+) Deposit		BALANCE
							2,895.00

23   *Bank Account Math*

Name _____

Answer the following questions.

1. The balance in Logan's checking account is $895.58. On Monday, he used his debit card to get gas for $25.97 and at the ATM machine to get $60.00 in cash. On Tuesday he wrote a check for groceries for $46.39.

   How much did Logan spend on Monday
   and Tuesday?   _____

   What is the current balance in his account?   _____

2. On Wednesday morning, an automatic deposit of $1,250.00 went into Logan's checking account. In the afternoon, he used his debit card to take some coworkers to lunch. He spent $58.69 and then spent $12.40 to take an Uber back to work.

   How much did he spend on lunch and the Uber?   _____

   After the deposit, and what he spent on lunch and
   the Uber, what is Logan's account balance?   _____

3. Amy has $5,645.00 in her savings account. She has $3,873.00 in her checking account. She withdrew $932.00 from her savings to pay for some dental work.

   What is the balance in her savings account?   _____

   How much more does she have in savings than
   in checking?   _____

4. Amy deposited two checks into her checking account, one for $64.98 and one for $362.60. Later that day, she used her debit card to pick up a prescription for $38.56 and to buy some groceries for $62.49.

   What is her checking account balance after
   her deposit?   _____

   After her purchases, what is her account balance?   _____

Name _____

Solve the problems and fill in the blanks.

1. Lily rents a three-bedroom apartment from Aztec Property Rentals. She has
    two roommates. Each roommate pays $368.00 per month. Lily pays twice that
    for her rent. Lily writes a check for the total rent.

**Fill in the check with today's date, the property company's name, and the rent
total. Sign the check.**

<table>
<tr><td>Lily Baker
2625 Orange Blossom Lane
Scottsdale, AZ 85260</td><td></td><td>3382</td></tr>
</table>

Lily Baker
2625 Orange Blossom Lane
Scottsdale, AZ 85260

3382

_____
Date

Pay to the
  order of _____ $ _____

_____ Dollars

Bank

For _____   _____

123456789 : 987654321   3382

2. Scott earns extra money walking dogs. He charges $38.00 per week.
    Mr. Lee wrote him a check (#2267) for three weeks. Mrs. Jones wrote him a
    check (#1380) for four weeks. Scott is depositing the checks into his checking
    account. He wants to get $58.00 in cash back.

Fill in the deposit slip to show his total deposit. Use today's date.

DEPOSIT TICKET

Scott McPhearson
548 E. Market St.
Greensboro, NC 27403

Date_____

_____
Sign here in teller's presence for cash received

Bank 123456789:987654321

						.		
Cash						.		
List Checks								
						.		
						.		
Total from Other Side						.		
SUBTOTAL						.		
Less Cash Received						.		
TOTAL						.		

Emma B. Harris

Birthday September 2, 1995
Social Security 555-22-1236

Personal Information

Rent $1,560.00 per month
Income $3,684.00 per month

Contact Information

Cell Phone 970-555-6642
Email eharris25@gmail.com

Bank Account Information

Rocky Mountain Bank	Checking Account Number	4556841599
Rocky Mountain Bank	Savings Account Number	4556841620

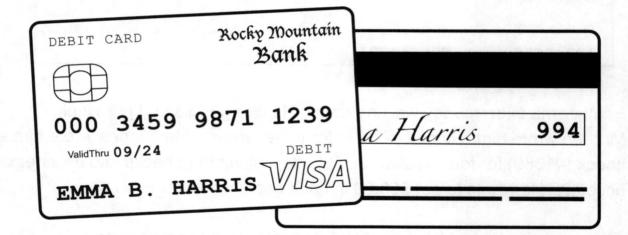

DEBIT CARD   Rocky Mountain Bank

000 3459 9871 1239

ValidThru 09/24   DEBIT VISA

EMMA B. HARRIS

a Harris   994

EMMA B. HARRIS
322 FIR ST. APT. 506
DENVER, CO 80022

572

_____ Date

Pay to the
order of _____ $ _____

_____ Dollars

Rocky Mountain Bank

For _____ _____

345678912 : 4556841599   572

Name _____

Answer the questions about Emma's bank account transactions. Use information from page 26 for some of the questions.

1. Emma gets paid twice a month. Half of her monthly income is automatically deposited on May 1. The other half is automatically deposited on May 15.

    How much is each deposit? _____

2   On May 8, Emma used her debit card to get a manicure and a deluxe pedicure from Main Street Day Spa. The manicure cost $15.00. The deluxe pedicure costs $55.00. She included a 20% tip.

    How much was charged to her card? _____

3. Emma took her friend to a movie at Regal Cinemas on May 12. The tickets cost $12.50 each. She bought a large tub of popcorn for them to share for $6.25. She also bought two large sodas for $3.20 each. She paid for it all with her debit card.

    How much was charged to her card? _____

4. On May 16, Emma used her debit card to take advantage of a 35% off sale at the Yard and Garden Store. She bought one outdoor table and four outdoor chairs for her patio. The regular price of the table was $184.00. The regular price for each chair was $65.00.

    With the discount, how much was charged to her card? _____

5. Emma's roommate Grace pays 1/3 of the rent. Grace gave Emma a check for her portion of the rent on May 28.

    How much was the deposit? _____

27

Name _____

Use the answers on page 27 to fill in the blanks on Emma's transaction register for the month of May. Add or subtract each transaction to keep a running total of the balance.

AD Automatic Deposit   **AP** Automatic Payment   **ATM** Teller Machine   **DC** Debit Card   **D** Deposit   **T** Transfer

Check# or Code	Date	Description of Transaction	(–) Payment		(+) Deposit		BALANCE 1,850.00	
AD	May 1	Paycheck						
1055	May 4	Denver Public Utilities	185	94				
	May 8							
DC	May 10	Freshie's Market	86	45				
	May 12							
DC	May 14	Shell Gas Station	32	28				
AD	May 15	Paycheck						
	May 16							
AP	May 18	Credit Card Payment	65	80				
ATM	May 20	Cash Withdrawal	80	00				
D	May 28	Rent from Grace						

1. What is the total for Emma's deposits? _____

2. How much more did she spend at the Yard and Garden Store than at Freshie's Market? _____

3. How much is the automatic payment? _____

Name _____

Answer the questions about Emma's savings account.

1. Emma's monthly income is $3,684.00. She puts 5% of that into savings each
    month.

    How much does Emma save each month?   _____

    How much does Emma save in a year?   _____

2. Emma has been saving money for four years.

    How much money is in her savings account? _____

    Emma is using half of her savings for a trip to
    Ireland. How much will she have to spend? _____

3. If Emma increases the amount she saves to 7%
    of her monthly income, how much more will
    she save each month?   _____

    How much more will she save in a year?   _____

4. Emma's mom told her she would contribute to her savings if Emma increased
    the amount she saved to 7%. Her mom will give her 1/2 that amount to add to
    her savings account each month.

    What would the total savings amount be
    each month?   _____

    What would the total savings amount be in a year? _____

5. Rocky Mountain bank wants to encourage savings. For a limited time they
    are offering to give a 5% bonus for each $1,000.00 saved. If Emma saves
    $5,000.00, she will get 5% of that amount as a bonus.

    How much will her bonus be?   _____

Name _____

Emma is shopping on Amazon with her debit card. While she is shopping, she wants to keep track of her checking account balance. Her current balance is $2,365.49. Answer the questions about her online purchases.

1.   Emma started out by adding some vitamin supplements to her shopping cart. She bought a bottle of Vitamin B12 for $12.65, a bottle of Vitamin C for $8.95 and two bottles of Multivitamins at $25.39 each.

     How much did she spend on vitamins?   _____

     After this purchase, what is her balance?   _____

2.   Amazon is having a 30% off sale on books. Emma bought three books with a regular price of $16.00 each, and two books with a regular price of $28.00 each.

     How much is saved on the book purchase?   _____

     What is the total spent on books?   _____

     After this purchase, what is her balance?   _____

Use Emma's debit card to fill out the form and complete her online transaction.

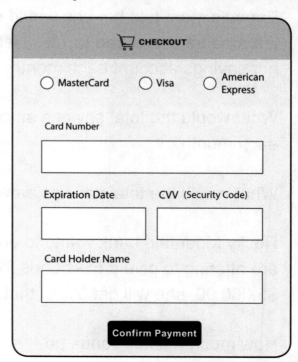

Name _____

Answer the questions.

1. Emma is going to visit her sister. She used her debit card to buy some gifts
    for her niece and nephew. She got her niece a puzzle for $14.95 and a set of
    watercolor pens for $18.99. She got her nephew an action figure for $13.27
    and a monster truck for $24.79. There is a 7% sales tax on her purchase.

    How much is her card charged for the gifts
    including tax?   _____

2. Emma had Ron's Landscaping do some work in her yard. He trimmed her
    trees for $370.00, dug a little pond for $650.00, and put in a gravel walkway for
    $495.00.

    How much did Ron charge for the work?   _____

    Emma was very happy with Ron's work so she
    added a 20% bonus. How much did Emma pay
    for the landscaping?   _____

**Emma wrote a check to Ron for his work. Fill in the blanks on the check below
with today's date, and the total for the landscaping. Sign the check.**

EMMA B. HARRIS	573
322 FIR ST. APT. 506	
DENVER, CO 80022	_____
	Date

Pay to the
  order of _____ $ _____

_____ Dollars

Rocky Mountain Bank

For _____   _____

    345678912 : 4556841599   573

3. Before Emma bought the gifts and had the landscaping done, the balance in
    her checking account was $2,942.00.

    What is her balance now?   _____

Lamar R. Patterson

Birthday August 10, 1989
Social Security 566-88-9200

Home & Personal Information

Mortgage $2,234.00 per month
Has owned this home for 4 years, 3 months.
Income $6,500.00 per month

Contact Information

Home Phone 503-222-9684
Cell Phone 503-555-8922
Email LamarP@windriver.com

Additional Information

Citizenship
U.S. Citizen

First School Attended
Irvington Elementary

Mother's Maiden Name
Wallace

OREGON DRIVER LICENSE

LIC# **PATTL18580MH**
NAME **PATTERSON**
LAMAR RASHID
DOB **08-10-1989**
ADDRESS **824 NE 10TH AVE**
PORTLAND, OR 97212
SEX **M**   HGT **6-02**
WGT **190**   EYES **BRN**

ISSUED **03-22-2016**

Lamar

SOCIAL SECURITY

566-88-9200
Lamar Rashid Patterson

Lamar Patterson
SIGNATURE
USA

PORTLAND GAS & ELECTRIC
P.O. Box 4438
Portland, OR 97208

LAMAR R. PATTERSON
824 NE 10TH AVE
PORTLAND, OR 97212

Name _____

Lamar is applying for a bank account. Use his information on page 32 to fill out the application.

APPLICANT INFORMATION		
APPLICANT NAME		
LAST	FIRST	MIDDLE
EMAIL		
ARE YOU AN EXISTING CUSTOMER? ○ YES ○ NO		

ADDRESS & PHONE			
RESIDENTIAL ADDRESS			
STREET	CITY	STATE	ZIP
HOW LONG HAVE YOU LIVED AT THIS ADDRESS?	HOME PHONE	BUSINESS PHONE (OPTIONAL)	CELL PHONE
MAILING ADDRESS (IF DIFFERENT FROM RESIDENTIAL)			
STREET	CITY	STATE	ZIP
PROOF OF ADDRESS ○ RENTAL LEASE	○ UTILITY BILL	○ MORTGAGE	○ OTHER

CITIZENSHIP & TAX REPORTING STATUS		
CITIZENSHIP STATUS ○ U.S. CITIZEN	○ NON-RESIDENT ALIEN	○ RESIDENT ALIEN
COUNTRY OF CITIZENSHIP(IF NON-U.S. RESIDENT		COUNTRY OF TAX REPORTING
DATE OF BIRTH	SOCIAL SECURITY NUMBER	

SECURITY INFORMATION	
NAME OF FIRST SCHOOL ATTENDED	MOTHER'S MAIDEN NAME

IDENTIFICATION (RECORD THE DRIVER'S LICENSE OR PASSPORT NUMBER)		
○ **DRIVER'S LICENSE**	○ **PASSPORT**	○ **BIRTH CERTIFICATE**

Name _____

Lamar's application was approved and he opened up a new bank account at Regence Bank.

Checking Account

Account Number: 442 389 6655

Opening Deposit: $2,450.00

Savings Account

Account Number: 442 389 7766

Opening Deposit: $3,280.00

When does Lamar's debit card expire?   _____

LAMAR PATTERSON
824 N.E. 10TH AVE.
PORTLAND, OR 97212

1011

_____
Date

Pay to the
order of _____ $ _____

_____ Dollars

REGENCE BANK

For _____   _____

567891234 : 4423896655   1011

What is Regence Bank's routing number?   _____

Name _____

Answer the questions about Lamar's bank account transactions.

1. On October 3, Lamar went to dinner at Rustica with some friends. The food and drinks cost $168.00. They added a 20% tip.

    How much was the total bill?   _____

    Lamar put 1/3 of the total on his debit card.
    How much was his card charged?   _____

2. Lamar's monthly income is $6,500.00. He gets paid four times a month.
    On October 6, October 12, October 19, and October 26, 1/4 of his monthly income will be automatically deposited.

    How much is each deposit?   _____

3. On October 13, Lamar went to Target to pick up a prescription. While he was there he got some cleaning products and office supplies. His prescription cost $24.65, the cleaning products cost $18.66, and the office supplies cost $28.30. He put the purchase on his debit card.

    How much was his card charged?   _____

4. Lamar is helping his sister Brittney pay her rent this month. Her rent is $1,320.00. He wrote check #1021 to her for half of her rent.

    What was the amount of the check he wrote?   _____

5. On October 20, Lamar used his debit card at Petco. He got a 20lb. bag of dog food for $44.55, a dog collar for $15.95, a dog toy for $25.65, and a chew bone for $6.98.

    How much was his card charged?   _____

Name _____

Use the answers on page 35 to fill in the blanks on Lamar's transaction register. Add or subtract each transaction to keep a running total of the balance.

AD Automatic Deposit   **AP** Automatic Payment   **ATM** Teller Machine   **DC** Debit Card   **D** Deposit   **T** Transfer

Check# or Code	Date	Description of Transaction	(–) Payment		(+) Deposit		BALANCE
							4,850.00
1019	10/01	Mortgage	2,234	00			
DC	10/03						
AD	10/06	Paycheck					
AP	10/08	Car Insurance	86	40			
ATM	10/09	Cash Withdrawal	120	00			
AD	10/12	Paycheck					
DC	10/13	Target					
1020	10/16	Electric Bill	216	39			
AD	10/19	Paycheck					
	10/20	Petco					
AD	10/26	Paycheck					
1021	10/28	Brittney Patterson					

1.   What is the total of the checks Lamar wrote?   _____

2.   What is the balance on 10/12?   _____

3.   How much was charged to his debit card?   _____

Name _____

REGENCE BANK

CHECKING ACCOUNT STATEMENT

Lamar Patterson   Account Number: 4423896655
624 N.E. 10th Ave.
Portland, OR 97212

Beginning Balance: $4,850.00

Date	Description of Transaction	Withdrawal	Deposit	Balance
10/1	Western Mortgage Co. #1019	$2,234.00		$2,616.00
10/3	Rustica DC	$67.20		$2,548.80
10/6	OHSU Medical Center AD		$1,625.00	$4,173.80
10/8	Geico Insurance AP	$86.40		$4,087.40
10/9	ATM Cash withdrawal	$120.00		$3,967.40
10/12	OHSU Medical Center AD		$1,625.00	$5,592.40
10/13	Target DC	$71.60		$5,520.79
10/16	Tri-County Electric #1020	$216.39		$5,304.40
10/19	OHSU Medical Center AD		$1,625.00	$6,929.40
10/20	Petco DC	$93.13		$6,836.27
10/20	ATM Cash Withdrawal	$80.00		$6,756.27
10/26	OHSU Medical Center AD		$1,625.00	$8,381.27
10/27	Big C Sports Center DC	$45.13		$8,336.14
10/28	Brittney Patterson #1021	$660.00		$7,676.14

Compare Lamar's account statement for October with his transaction register on page 36. List any differences.

_____

_____

_____

Name _____

Answer the questions. Use information from page 32.

1. Lamar decides to pay extra on his mortgage for 6 months. He is paying 30% more than his regular payment.

    How much is each payment?   _____

    How much will he pay in 6 months?   _____

2. Lamar asked his boss for a 12% raise. If he gets his raise, how much more will he make each month?   _____

    How much more will he make each year?   _____

3. If he gets his raise, Lamar will save half of it each month. He will add that amount to his current monthly savings of $450.00.

    How much will go into savings each month?   _____

    How much will he save each year?   _____

4. Lamar has $5,980.00 in his savings account. He's going on vacation to the San Juan Islands with his girlfriend. He bought two plane tickets to Friday Harbor for $365.00 each. He booked an Airbnb for four nights at $285.00 per night.

    How much did he spend for the vacation?   _____

    He transferred money out of his savings to pay for the vacation. How much is left in his savings?   _____

Mia S. Cho

Birthday February 2, 1984
Social Security 888-12-3456

Personal Information

Mortgage $1,895.00 per month
Income $5,650.00 per month

Contact Information

Cell Phone 615-555-8922
Email miacho@yahoo.com

Bank Account Information

First National Bank	Checking Account Number	6243228944
First National Bank	Savings Account Number	6243228945

DEBIT CARD · 1st National Bank

110 4460 0853 3412

ValidThru 03/26

DEBIT VISA

MIA S. CHO

241

MIA S. CHO
3455 CIRCLE PLACE
NASHVILLE, TN 37206

1900

Date

Pay to the
order of _____ $ _____

_____ Dollars

1st National Bank

For _____

356789124 : 6243228944   1900

Name _____

Answer the questions about Mia's checking account transactions. Use information from page 39 for some of the questions.

1. Mia's paycheck is automatically deposited into her checking account. She gets paid twice a month on the 5th and the 20th.

    How much is each deposit?   _____

2. Mia's mortgage payment is automatically taken out of her checking account on the 1st of the month. She just increased her mortgage payment by 20%.

    How much is her current payment?   _____

3. On February 8, Mia went shopping for some new clothes at Vintage Creations. She bought a sweater for $62.50, a skirt for $32.95, two blouses for $24.98 each and a pair of jeans for $46.39. She put the purchases on her debit card.

    How much was her card charged?   _____

4. Mia used her debit card to buy tickets to the ballet on February 19 for herself and two of her friends. Each ticket cost $128.00.

    How much was her card charged?   _____

5. Mia deposited three checks into her account using an ATM machine. The first check was for $286.45. The second check was for $159.34. The third check was for $218.96.

    How much was the total deposit?   _____

Name _____

Use the answers on page 40 to fill in the blanks on Mia's transaction register.
Add or subtract each transaction to keep a running total of the balance.

Check# or Code	Date	Description of Transaction	(–) Payment		(+) Deposit		BALANCE 3,650.00	
	Feb. 1	Mortgage						
ATM	Feb. 3	ATM Cash Withdrawal	80	00				
AD	Feb. 5	Paycheck						
DC	Feb. 8	Vintage Creations						
AP	Feb. 10	Phone Bill	118	30				
DC	Feb. 12	Fred's Fish House	88	45				
	Feb. 19	Nashville Ballet						
1066	Feb. 20	Water Bill	128	39				
AD	Feb. 20	Paycheck						
ATM	Feb. 22	ATM Deposit						

1. How much more did Mia spend at the ballet than at Fred's Fish House?   _____

2. What is the total for the mortgage, phone bill, and water bill?   _____

3. Which transaction is for $191.80?   _____

4. What is the difference between the ending balance and the beginning balance?   _____

Name _____

Answer the questions.

1. Mia went to Nashville Clinic for some X-rays and lab work. Her X-rays cost $1,650.00. Her insurance paid 80% of the cost. She had to pay the balance. Her insurance paid for most of her lab work but she had a $35.00 co-pay.

    How much was her bill?   _____

Mia wrote a check to the clinic. Fill in the blanks on the check below with today's date and the total for the bill. Sign the check.

```
┌──────────────────────────────────────────────────────────────────────┐
│  MIA S. CHO                                                    1901    │
│  3455 CIRCLE PLACE                                                     │
│  NASHVILLE, TN 37206             _____           │
│                                                          Date          │
│  Pay to the                                                           │
│    order of  _____  $ _____  │
│                                                                        │
│  _____ Dollars     │
│                                                                        │
│  1st National Bank                                                    │
│                                                                        │
│  For _____        _____       │
│      356789124   :   6243228944         1901                          │
└──────────────────────────────────────────────────────────────────────┘
```

2. Mia and her three sisters all chipped in to send their parents to Europe for their anniversary. With airfare and hotels, the total cost was $5,860.00. Each sister paid 1/4 of the cost.

    How much did Mia owe?   _____

    Mia has $4,849.00 in savings. She transferred
    money from her savings to pay for the trip.
    How much is left in savings?   _____

3. Mia built a temporary little fence in her back yard to keep wild rabbits out of her garden. She bought 25 feet of chicken wire at $2.32 per foot. She also bought 16 wooden stakes at 89¢ each. She bought a staple gun to attach the chicken wire to the stakes for $16.95. She put the items on her debit card.

    How much was charged to her card?   _____

Name _____

Mia wants to create a personal PayPal account to make it easier and safer to purchase things online. She will register her debit card for payment. Each time she uses PayPal, her debit card will be charged.

Use information from page 39 to fill out the online PayPal form.

Sign up for free!	**Welcome!**
	Let's create your account.

O Personal account
O Business account

Street address

┌─────────────────────────────┐
└─────────────────────────────┘

Legal first name

┌─────────────────────────────┐
└─────────────────────────────┘

City

┌─────────────────────────────┐
└─────────────────────────────┘

Legal last name

┌─────────────────────────────┐
└─────────────────────────────┘

State

┌─────────────────────────────┐
└─────────────────────────────┘

Your email

┌─────────────────────────────┐
└─────────────────────────────┘

Zip code

┌─────────────────────────────┐
└─────────────────────────────┘

Create your password

┌─────────────────────────────┐
└─────────────────────────────┘

Phone number

┌─────────────────────────────┐
└─────────────────────────────┘

8 characters or more.
At least one number or symbol. (like @#&!)

NEXT   **NEXT**

Just link your debit card so you can shop.

Debit card number

┌─────────────────────────────┐
└─────────────────────────────┘

Security code

┌─────────────────────────────┐
└─────────────────────────────┘

Expiration date

┌─────────────────────────────┐
└─────────────────────────────┘

LINK CARD

Name _____

Mia is shopping online using her new PayPal account. She needs to keep track of her checking account balance. Each purchase will come directly out of her account. Her current balance is $3,620.00.

Answer the questions about her purchases.

1. Mia went to the Etsy website to buy some gifts. She bought a necklace for $185.40, two pairs of earrings for $45.99 ea., and a vintage hair clip for $24.65. She found some beautiful hand painted greeting cards and bought 8 for $8.95 each.

   How much was charged to her PayPal account?   _____

   After this purchase, what is her balance?   _____

2. Mia's favorite shoe store is having an online special. If you buy two pairs of shoes, you get 20% off. If you buy three or more pairs of shoes, you get 40% off. Mia bought 2 pairs of athletic shoes for $65.00 each, one pair of sandals for $52.00, and a pair of flip flops for $18.50.

   With the discount, how much was charged to
   her PayPal account?   _____

   After this purchase, what is her balance?   _____

3. Bed, Bath & Beyond is having a bedding sale. Mia bought two pillows that are on sale for $10.99; regular price $16.00. She bought a comforter for $135.00; regular price $269.99. She also bought a set of sheets for $69.99; regular price $128.00.

   How much did she save on her purchases?   _____

   How much was charged to her PayPal account?   _____

   After this purchase, what is her balance?   _____

Javier C. Lopez

Birthday November 7, 1983
Social Security 777-21-6543

Personal Information
Mortgage $1,588.00 per month
Income $84,000.00 per year

Contact Information
Cell Phone 254-555-16802
Email jlopez@bayloru.com

Bank Account Information

Central Texas Bank	Checking Account Number	1778643347
Central Texas Bank	Savings Account Number	1778643358

DEBIT CARD **CENTRAL TEXAS ★ BANK**

100 0423 9871 1298

ValidThru 05/25 DEBIT VISA

JAVIER LOPEZ

er Lopez 338

JAVIER LOPEZ
6445 ASH ST.
WACO, TX 76706

2034

Date

Pay to the order of _____ $ _____

_____ Dollars

CENTRAL TEXAS ★ BANK

For _____ _____

567891249 : 1778643347 2034

Name _____

Answer the questions about Javier's checking account transactions.
Use information from page 45 for some of the questions.

1. How much is Javier's monthly income?   _____

2. He gets paid twice a month, on the 10th and the 25th. His paycheck is
    automatically deposited.

    How much is each deposit?   _____

3. Javier just started a new savings program. Twice a month, on the 11th and the
    26th, he will transfer 12% of his paycheck into his savings account.

    How much will each transfer be?   _____

    How much will he save in a year?   _____

4. Once a month Javier goes to Costco to stock up on supplies. This month he
    spent $235.89 on groceries, $86.40 on supplements, $68.35 on clothes, and
    $42.36 on cleaning supplies. He put this purchase on his debit card.

    How much was his card charged?   _____

    His membership includes a 2% cash back reward on
    the amount of the purchases he makes. How much
    will his reward be for this purchase?   _____

5. Javier has three automatic payments that come out of his checking account
    each month. On the 1st, is his mortgage payment for $1,588.00. On the 5th, is
    his car payment for $289.50. On the 14th is his credit card payment of $156.40.

    What is the total of his automatic payments?   _____

Name _____

Use the answers on page 46 to fill in the blanks on Javier's transaction register. Add or subtract each transaction to keep a running total of the balance.

AD Automatic Deposit   **AP** Automatic Payment   **ATM** Teller Machine   **DC** Debit Card   **D** Deposit   **T** Transfer

Check# or Code	Date	Description of Transaction	(−) Payment		(+) Deposit		BALANCE 4,003.56	
2033	Sept. 1	Mortgage	1,588	00				
AP	Sept. 5	Car Payment	289	50				
AD	Sept. 10	Paycheck						
ATM	Sept. 10	Cash Withdrawal	200	00				
T	Sept. 11	Transfer to Savings						
AP	Sept. 14	Credit Card	156	40				
DC	Sept. 18	Costco						
2034	Sept. 19	Utility Bill	210	49				
ATM	Sept. 20	ATM Deposit			325	00		
AD	Sept. 25	Paycheck						
T	Sept. 26	Transfer to Savings						

1.   What is Javier's balance on September 14?   _____

2.   How much more is the car payment than the
     utility bill?   _____

3.   What is the total of his deposits?   _____

4.   How much more is the ending balance than
     the beginning balance?   _____

Name _____

Use information from page 45 to answer the questions.

1. Javier works for Baylor University. His mortgage is with BCM Credit Union.
    Starting in October, he is increasing his mortgage payment by 40%.

    How much more will he be paying each month?   _____

    How much is his new payment?   _____

Fill out the check to his credit union for his new mortgage payment for October 1.

```
┌─────────────────────────────────────────────────────────────┐
│  JAVIER LOPEZ                                        2034     │
│  6445 ASH ST.                                                │
│  WACO, TX 76706          _____            │
│                                              Date            │
│  Pay to the                                                  │
│    order of  _____  $ _____  │
│                                                              │
│  _____ Dollars│
│  CENTRAL                                                     │
│  TEXAS ★ BANK                                               │
│  For _____    _____        │
│   567891249  :  1778643347      2034                        │
└─────────────────────────────────────────────────────────────┘
```

2. After increasing his payment, how much more
    will Javier pay toward his mortgage in a year?   _____

3. Javier put in a request for a transfer to another department at the university.
    If he gets the transfer, it will mean a 15% raise.

    How much more will he make each month?   _____

    How much more will he make in a year?   _____

    What will his new monthly income be?   _____

    What will his new yearly income be?   _____

Name _____

Answer the following questions.

1. Javier used his debit card to take his family to the Cameron Park Zoo. There were three adults, one senior, and three kids ages 5, 8, and 9.

TICKET PRICING	
Children (Ages 3 & Under):	FREE
Children (Ages 4-12):	$7.⁰⁰
Adults (Ages 13+):	$10.⁰⁰
Sr. Citizens (Ages 60+):	$9.⁰⁰

Based on the ticket prices, how much was his card charged?   _____

2. Javier went to the ATM to get $240.00 in cash. He used some of the money to take two of his friends to a Baylor football game. The tickets cost $29.00 each.

How much did he spend on the tickets?   _____

How much cash was left?   _____

3. Javier used his debit card to pay for a fishing trip for himself and three friends. The trip cost $1,728.00. His friends paid him back for their portion of the trip. Jim wrote a check (#788) for 1/4 of the cost. Al wrote a check (#965) for 1/4 of the cost. Will paid cash for 1/4 of the cost.

Fill out the deposit slip to show how much Javier deposited into his checking account. Use today's date.

DEPOSIT TICKET			Cash						.		
JAVIER LOPEZ			List Checks								
6445 ASH ST.											
WACO, TX 76706			_____						.		
Date_____			_____						.		
			Total from Other Side						.		
_____			**SUBTOTAL**						.		
Sign here in teller's presence for cash received			Less Cash Received						.		
CENTRAL TEXAS ★ BANK 567891249:1778643347			**TOTAL**						.		

Name _____

Javier is signing up for online banking so he can easily check his bank account transactions and balance.

Use information from page 45 to fill out the online registration form. Choose a Username and Password for him and answer the three security questions using your personal information.

CENTRAL
TEXAS ★ BANK

Online Registration

Social Security Number

[   ]

Debit Card Number

[   ]

Checking Account Number

[   ]

Account Information

Email

[   ]

Create Username

[   ]

Create Password

[   ]

8 characters or more.
At least one number or symbol. (@*#&!)

Help us keep your account secure.

What is your favorite animal?

[   ]

What city were you born in?

[   ]

What is the name of your best friend?

[   ]

REGISTER

Name _____

Javier wants to set up an automatic payment for the 10th of each month to pay his car insurance. He wants to make the payment with an eCheck.

Use information below and from page 45 to fill out the eCheck form.

CAR SHIELD
Affordable vehicle & driver protection.

INSURANCE BILL

Javier Lopez
6445 Ash St.
Waco, TX 76706

Total Amount Owed	$1,050.10
Monthly Amount Owed	$87.51
Due Date	October 12
Policy Number	AA098124LOPEZ

Method of Payment

How would you like to pay?

○ Credit Card   ○ eCheck   ○ PayPal

eCheck

Bank Name

_____

Bank Routing Number

_____

Name of Account Holder

_____

Account Number

_____

Payee

_____

Amount

_____

Date of Payment

_____

Recurring Payment

○ Yes   ○ No

Name _____

Fill in the transaction register below. Add or subtract each transaction to keep a running total of the balance.

Check #2066	Nov. 1	Mortgage	– $1,860.00
ATM	Nov. 5	ATM Deposit	+ $395.42
Debit Card	Nov. 8	Tony's Pizzaria	– $64.20
Check #2067	Nov. 9	Car Payment	– $259.64
Debit Card	Nov. 10	Ralph's Market	– $98.35
Automatic Deposit	Nov. 10	Paycheck	+ $2,890.00
Debit Card	Nov.16	Amazon	– $28.66
Debit Card	Nov. 20	Macy's	– $147.85
Transfer	Nov. 23	Transfer to savings	– $250.00
Automatic Deposit	Nov. 25	Paycheck	+ $2,890.00

AD Automatic Deposit   **AP** Automatic Payment   **ATM** Teller Machine   **DC** Debit Card   **D** Deposit   **T** Transfer

Check# or Code	Date	Description of Transaction	(–) Payment	(+) Deposit	BALANCE	
					3,225.00	

Name _____

Answer the questions.

1.   Carter makes $63,000.00 per year. His paycheck is automatically deposited twice a month.

How much does Carter make each month?   _____

How much is each deposit?   _____

2.   The balance in Carter's checking account is $5,489.33. On Friday, he got $280.00 in cash from the ATM machine. On Saturday, he put $143.68 on his debit card to buy some paint and $74.25 to go out to dinner.

How much did Carter spend on Friday
and Saturday?   _____

What is the balance in his account?   _____

3.   An automatic rent payment for $1,875.00 came
out of Carter's checking account today. What is the
new balance in his account?   _____

4.   Carter saves 15% of his paycheck each month.
How much does he save every month?   _____

He has been saving the same amount every month
for three years. How much does he have in savings?_____

5.   If Carter uses 1/3 of his savings for a down payment
on a car, how much will his down payment be?   _____

How much will be left in his savings account?   _____

GLOSSARY

access	to get or make use of something
account number	a unique number given to a checking or savings account
account statement	a record of activity on a particular account
ATM	an automated teller machine is a machine that allows you to electronically access your checking account; get cash, make deposits, and check the balance
automatic bill pay	a money transfer scheduled on a particular date to pay a recurring bill
balance	the amount of money on hand
debit card	a plastic payment card connected to a checking account that can be used instead of cash when making purchases
deposit	put money in the bank
direct deposit	an electronic payment from one bank account to another
eCheck	an electronic check connected to a checking account
identification	something used to show who a person is
fraud	the tricking of someone in order to cheat
magnetic stripe	a black, brown or silver strip of magnetic information found on the back of a debit or credit card
microchip	a small, thin piece of material with tiny electronic parts found on the front of a debit or credit card
mobile app	a type of application software designed to run on a mobile device, such as a smartphone or tablet
money transfer	moving money from one account to another electronically

password	a secret word or phrase that must be used to gain access to a computer system, network or online account
payee	a person to whom money is paid; a person or business to whom a check is made payable
PIN	a personal identification number given to someone to make electronic transactions with a debit card possible
POS terminal	a card reader that a retailer uses to record a sale and initiate payment approval
routing number	a nine-digit code that's based on the U.S. Bank location where an account was opened. It's the first set of numbers printed on the bottom of your checks, on the left side
security code	a three-digit number printed on the back of a debit card
security questions	questions, only you would know the answer to, used for online banking to help keep your account secure
transaction	to carry out a business exchange
transaction register	a booklet where withdrawals and deposits for a checking account can be recorded
username	a unique series of characters used to identify a user and allow access to a computer system, network, or online account
withdraw	to take money out of an account
withdrawals	money taken out of the bank

Name _____

Choose the word or phrase from the word box that matches each definition. Write it on the blank line.

deposit	identification	money transfer	transaction
eCheck	microchip	routing number	username

1. moving money from one account to another electronically

    _____

2. put money in the bank

    _____

3. an electronic check connected to a bank account

    _____

4. a unique series of characters used to identify someone trying to access an online account

    _____

5. something used to show who a person is

    _____

6. a nine-digit code for the bank printed on the bottom of checks

    _____

7. to carry out a business exchange

    _____

8. a small, thin piece of electronic material on the front of a debit card

    _____

Name _____

Choose the word or phrase from the word box that matches each definition. Write it on the blank line.

access	fraud	POS terminal
account statement	password	
balance	payee	withdraw

1. a secret word or phrase to gain access to an online account

    _____

2. to take money out of an account

    _____

3. a card reader in stores for debit and credit card payments

    _____

4. the tricking of someone in order to cheat

    _____

5. a person or business to whom a check is made payable

    _____

6. to get or make use of something

    _____

7. a record of activity on a particular account

    _____

8. the amount of money on hand

    _____

Use a word or phrase from the box to complete each sentence. Not all words or phrases will be used.

ATM	identification	security questions
automatic bill pay	password	transaction register
balance	PIN	username

1. Connor used the _____ at the store to get some cash.

2. Melanie recorded every check she wrote in her _____.

3. Josh always checks the _____ in his account before he uses his debit card.

4. Andrew used his driver's license as _____ to open up a bank account.

5. You have to answer _____ if you want to set up online banking.

6. Pam uses _____ to pay her phone bill each month.

7. To use your debit card at the grocery store, you must first enter your _____.

Use a word or phrase from the box to complete each sentence. Not all words or phrases will be used.

account statement	microchip	routing number
deposit	money transfer	username
fraud	payee	withdraw

1. Mike inserted the _____ into the POS terminal to pay for his purchase.

2. Jill used a _____ to take money from her checking account and put it in her savings account.

3. Ben always compares his monthly _____ with his transaction register.

4. To create an eCheck, you will need the bank's _____ and your account number.

5. Parkrose Hardware is the _____ on the check.

6. Joe had to create a _____ and password to open up a PayPal account.

7. Sandy used her debit card to _____ money from her account.

PAGE 4

1) A bank account is for everyday use; a savings account is for holding money for future use. 2) driver's license, passport, state ID, birth certificate 3) It's convenient and safe. 4) by showing a lease, mortgage papers or a utility bill 5) to keep track of deposits and withdrawals 6) They compare it with your signature when you write or deposit a check. 7) between $25 and $100 8) a debit card, personalized checks

PAGE 9

1) ATM deposit, deposit slips, automatic deposit 2) checks and cash to be deposited 3) Debit cards use your money; credit cards use borrowed money 4) immediately 5) numbers and words 6) to keep your account safe 7) microchip, name, expiration date, account number, bank name 8) *Answers will vary.*

PAGE 13

1) in person, mobile app, online 2) withdraw cash, make a deposit, check your account balance 3) enter your PIN 4) banks, grocery stores, drug stores, etc. 5) electronic card reader that records sales and gets payment approval 6) reads card information and checks to see if funds are available for the purchase 7) choose debit 8) The machine will make a sound.

PAGE 14

so that you will always know how much money you have in your account

PAGE 16

There is an extra ATM cash withdrawal for $40 that changes the ending balance to $2,468.83.

PAGE 17

1) a booklet where you record the withdrawals and deposits for a checking account 2) the amount of money you have to spend after each transaction 3) AD=automatic deposit, AP= automatic payment, DC=debit card, D= deposit 4) to pay the utility bill 5) $2,462.28 6) the amount of money your start out with 7) It shows a listing of the withdrawals and deposits the bank has recorded for your checking account. 8) to catch any mistakes

PAGE 20

1) register for online banking 2) username, password 3) your account number, bank routing number 4) enter your username and password 5) you can see your account every day 6) You choose a day each month to have money automatically withdrawn from your account to pay a recurring bill. 7) an electronic way to pay, send money, or accept payments 8) create a username and password, register a way to pay for purchases

PAGE 21

1) B 2) A 3) A 4) D 5) C 6) B 7) A 8) C

PAGE 22

1) Check to Met Market for $26.69 2) Deposit ticket: 55.00, 110.00, 110.00, 275.00

PAGE 23

AP	7/1	rent	1,050.00	1,845.00
ATM	7/3	cash	120.00	1,725.00
105	7/5	PUD	155.00	1,570.00
106	7/8	Met Market	27.69	1,542.31
DC	7/10	City Garden Café	44.13	1,498.18
AD	7/15	paycheck	3,450.00	4,948.18
DC	7/18	Rexall	13.45	4,934.73
DC	7/20	Costco	159.85	4,774.88
DC	7/22	Arco gas	32.15	4,742.73
D	7/22	Refund check	156.98	4,899.71

PAGE 24

1) $132.36, $763.22 2) $71.09, $1,942.13 3) $4,713.00, $840.00 4) $4,300.58, $4,199.53

PAGE 25

1) Check to Aztec Property Rentals for $1,472.00 2) Deposit ticket: 114.00, 152.00, 266.00, 208.00

PAGE 27

1) $1,842.00 2) $84.00 3) $37.65 4) $288.60 5) $520.00

PAGE 28

Payments	Deposits	Balance
	1,842.00	3,692.00
		3,506.06
84.00		3,422.06
		3,335.61
37.65		3,297.96
		3,265.68
	1,842.00	5,107.68
288.60		4,819.08
		4,753.28
		4,673.28
520.00		5,193.28

1) $4,204.00 2) $202.15 3) $65.80

PAGE 29

1) $184.20, $2,210.40 2) $8,841.60, $4,420.80 3) $73.68, $884.16 4) $386.82, $4,641.84 5) $250.00

PAGE 30

1) $72.38, $2,293.11 2) $31.20, $72.80, $2,220.31

PAGE 31

1) $77.04 2) $1,515.00, $1,818.00 3) $1,046.96

PAGE 34

10/26, 567891234

PAGE 35

1) $201.60, $67.20   **2)** $1,625.00   **3)** $71.61   **4)** $660.00
5) $93.13

PAGE 36

Payments	Deposits	Balance
		2,616.00
67.20		2,548.80
	1,625.00	4,173.80
		4,087.40
		3,967.40
	1,625.00	5,592.40
71.61		5,520.79
		5,304.40
	1,625.00	6,929.40
93.13		6,836.27
	1,625.00	8,461.27
660.00		7,801.27

1) $3,110.39   **2)** $5,592.40   **3)** $231.94

PAGE 37

cash withdrawal of $80.00, debit card transaction of $45.13, balance of $7,676.14

PAGE 38

1) $2,904.20, $17,425.20   **2)** $780.00, $9,360.00
3) $840.00, $10,080.00   **4)** $1,870.00, $4,110.00

PAGE 40

1) $2,825.00   **2)** $2,274.00   **3)** $191.80   **4)** $384.00
5) $664.75

PAGE 41

Payments	Deposits	Balance
2,274.00		1,376.00
		1,296.00
	2,285.00	4,121.00
191.80		3,929.20
		3,810.90
		3,722.45
384.00		3,338.45
		3,210.06
	2,825.00	6,035.06
	664.75	6,699.81

1) $295.55   **2)** $2,520.69   **3)** Vintage Creations
4) $3,049.81

PAGE 42

1) $365.00   **2)** $1,465.00, $3,384.00   **3)** $89.19

PAGE 43

PAGE 44

1) $373.63, $3,246.37   **2)** $120.30, $3,126.07
3) $203.02, $226.97, $2,899.10

PAGE 46

1) $7,000.00   **2)** $3,500.00   **3)** $420.00, $10,080.00
4) $433.00, $8.66   **5)** $2.033.90

PAGE 47

Payments	Deposits	Balance
		2,415.56
		2,126.06
	3,500.00	5,626.06
		5,426.06
420.00		5,006.06
		4,849.66
433.00		4,416.66
		4,206.17
		4,531.17
	3,500.00	8,031.17
420.00		7,611.17

1) $4,849.66   **2)** $79.01   **3)** $7,325.00   **4)** $3,607.61

PAGE 48

1) $635.20   **2)** $2,223.20   **3)** $7,622.40   **4)** $1,050.00,
$12,600.00, $8,050.00, $96,600.00

PAGE 49

1) $60.00 2) $87.00 3) $153.00 4) Deposit ticket: #788 432.00, #965 432.00, 432.00, 1,296.00

PAGE 50

CENTRAL
TEXAS ★ BANK

Online Registration

Social Security Number
777-21-6543

Debit Card Number
100042398711298

Checking Account Number
1778643347

Account Information

Email
jlopez@bayloru.com

Create Username
Answers will vary.

Create Password
Answers will vary.

8 characters or more.
At least one number or symbol. (@*#&!)

Help us keep your account secure.

What is your favorite animal?
Answers will vary.

What city were you born in?
Answers will vary.

What is the name of your best friend?
Answers will vary.

REGISTER

PAGE 51

Method of Payment

How would you like to pay?
○ Credit Card ● eCheck ○ PayPal

eCheck

Bank Name
Central Texas Bank

Bank Routing Number
567891249

Name of Account Holder
Javier Lopez

Account Number
1778643347

Payee
Car Shield

Amount
$87.51

Date of Payment
October 12

Recurring Payment
● Yes ○ No

PAGE 52

2066	11/1	Mortgage	1,860.00		1,365.00
ATM	11/5	Deposit		395.42	1,760.42
DC	11/8	Tony's	64.20		1,696.22
2067	11/9	Car Payment	259.64		1,436.58
DC	11/10	Ralph's	98.35		1,338.23
AD	11/10	Paycheck		2,890.00	4,228.23
DC	11/16	Amazon	28.66		4,199.57
DC	11/20	Macy's	147.85		4,051.72
T	11/23	Savings	250.00		3,801.72
AD	11/25	Paycheck		2,890.00	6,691.72

PAGE 53

1) $5,250.00, $2,625.00 2) $497.93, $4,991.40
3) $3,116.40 4) $787.50, $28,350.00 5) $9,450.00, $18,900.00

PAGE 56

1) money transfer 2) deposit 3) eCheck 4) username
5) identification 6) routing number 7) transaction
8) microchip

PAGE 57

1) password 2) withdraw 3) POS terminal 4) fraud
5) payee 6) access 7) account statement 8) balance

PAGE 58

1) ATM 2) transaction register 3) balance 4) identification
5) security questions 6) automatic bill pay 7) PIN

PAGE 59

1) microchip 2) money transfer 3) account statement
4) routing number 5) payee 6) username 7) withdraw